Thumb Position for the Cello

Book One

by Cassia Harvey

CHP107

www.charveypublications.com - print books

www.learnstrings.com - PDF downloadable books

www.harveystringarrangements.com - chamber music

Thumb Position for the Cello

Book One

Finger Position One: "Whole Step," "Whole Step," "Half Step."

Practice Suggestions

1. Place the thumb on its side, across two strings.

2. Play on the tips of the remaining fingers.

3. Keep the left wrist straight to support the hand and the thumb.

4. Press the string down completely with the thumb to build strength.

5. Play with full bows and strong tone.

Thumb Position for the Cello

Book One

Cassia Harvey

1.

2.

3.

4.

5.

6

Note: When you see 4th finger on G (in measure 3), shift back to fourth position on the A string. When you see 3rd finger on G (as in measure 4), play the note across on the D string, in thumb position.

Thumb Position for the Cello, Book One

6.

©2004 C. Harvey Publications All Rights Reserved.

7.

8.

9.

10.

11. A new place to use the thumb

12.

13.

14.

15.

16. A new place to use the thumb

17.

18.

19.

20.

21.

22.

23.

24.

25.

26.

27.

28.

29.

30.

Thumb Position in D Major

Cassia Harvey

Intonation Study

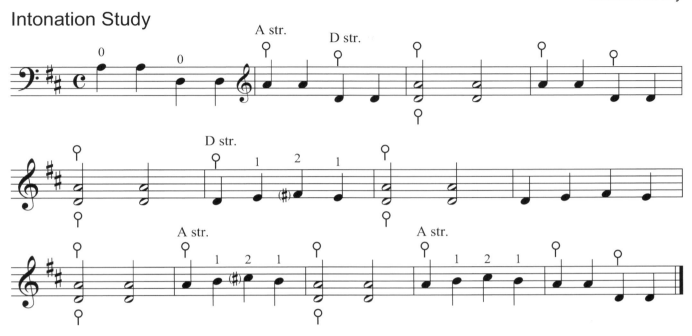

Finger Exercise

Thumb Position School for Cello

3

Down By the Station

Trad., arr. Harvey

A string

The Grey Goose

Trad., arr. Harvey

D string

Made in United States
Orlando, FL
13 March 2023